THANK☺YOU

written by Felicia Walker   illustrated by Brian Walker

DaBaDe Publishing

DaBaDe Publishing
Oakland, California
Text copyright 2003 by Felicia Walker
Illustrations copyright 2003 by Brian Walker
Book design by Brian Walker
Printed in Hong Kong

Library of Congress Control Number: 2004094741

Thank You / by Felicia Walker: Illustrated by Brian Walker
Summary: Learning to be thankful from the heart of a child.
ISBN 0-9747478-0-7
www.dabade.com

Dedicated to our inspirations
Niambi and Brea

Thank you Elmira, Thomas, and Lila without you this would not have been possible.
Thank you Granny, Pa Pa, Ruth and Momma we love you and miss you.

In everything we give thanks, much love. Felicia / Brian

www.dabade.com

elephants, dogs, and bears !

with toys galore in there!.

music helps with that too!

that I play with everyday!

for stories, learning and fun !

friends and family too !

Thank you for the love they give...

and the love I get from you!

for the blessings in my life !

The magic word is thank you...